Collecting and Photographing Your MICROZOO

Collecting and
Photographing Your

MICROZOO

Roy Pinney

THE WORLD PUBLISHING COMPANY

Cleveland and New York

The author and The World Publishing Company wish to thank the following individuals and institutions whose photographs have been used in this book:

Roy M. Allen, Sc.D., Bloomfield, New Jersey, pp. 16, 17, 22, 32
The American Museum of Natural History, pp. 15, 28, 59
Bausch & Lomb, Rochester, New York, p. 14
Carolina Biological Supply Co., Burlington, North Carolina, pp. 17, 29
Walter Dawn, from the National Audubon Society, pp. 13, 20
Eastman Kodak Co., pp. 16, 54
Dr. John J. Lee, The American Museum of Natural History, pp. 20, 21
M. B. Mittleman, p. 46
Hugh Spencer, from the National Audubon Society, p. 33
Dr. Roman Vishniac, p. 34

and Kenneth Bobrowsky and The Bronx High School of Science, for permitting the author to take photographs in the classroom

Published by The World Publishing Company
2231 West 110th Street, Cleveland 2, Ohio
Published simultaneously in Canada by
Nelson, Foster & Scott Ltd.
Library of Congress Catalog Card Number: 65-19722
FIRST EDITION
M W P
Designed by Jack Jaget

CONTENTS

Collecting and Photographing Your MICROZOO

TAKING A CLOSER LOOK AT LIFE

No zoo in the world has as many unusual creatures as the "micro-zoo." The tiny animals in it, seen under the microscope, display an astonishing variety. Some seem to be mere blobs that change shape as you watch them. Others, swaying delicately in the water, look like beautiful flowers. Still others grow in long chains or form globular colonies. Some of the animals will split in two to form two complete animals, and if you are patient you will actually see them do it.

Thousands of different specimens for your microzoo can be collected in your own home town—even in your own back yard, for, unlike larger animals which are found usually in limited areas, microzoo specimens are everywhere.

They live high in the atmosphere and in the depths of the sea. They swarm through tropical jungles and flourish at the South Pole. They are certainly the hardiest of creatures. They multiply rapidly and easily. Drop a single protozoan into water and within weeks he will have produced a million carbon copies of himself.

Building your own microzoo can be a fascinating project, and not really a difficult one.

In this book, these "animals you can't see" are described, and instructions are given about how to collect them and keep them alive and how to photograph them for a permanent collection.

The accompanying photographs show what you can see when you examine your microzoo specimens through a simple, inexpensive microscope.

Do you ever think about what "life" is? Do you wonder what makes a bird—a dog—a tree—alive, in contrast to a rock, or metal, or water? All living things need food and water; all respire; all grow. But what do they have in common that makes them live?

People have always wondered about this; scientists are still trying to solve the riddle of life.

Biologists—scientists who study life and living matter—could not investigate the structure of living things in detail until the microscope was invented.

In 1665 Robert Hooke took a piece of cork, sliced off a thin section of it, and examined it under his microscope. He reported that the cork was composed of some sixty little compartments, or **cells**, for every one-eighteenth of an inch. There were over a billion of them in one cubic inch! Actually the "compartments" Hooke was viewing were not cells at all, because they had long since dried out. Only the walls of the cells remained.

It was not until 1835 that a Frenchman, Félix Dujardin, discovered that a liquid substance filled each living cell. He called this substance "sarcode"; today it is known as **protoplasm**.

Between 1838 and 1839 two German scientists, Matthias Schleiden and Theodor Schwann, announced that all animals and plants are composed of cells. This was one of the first statements of the cell theory, which says that: (1) the cell is the basic unit of **structure** of all living things; (2) the cell is the unit of **function** of all living things; and (3) all cells come from other cells. Thus, as a basic unit or building block, the cell is to biologists something like what the atom is to the chemist and physicist.

The protoplasm of cells has been analyzed and found to consist of approximately 70 per cent water; the remaining substances are proteins, sugars, starches, fats, and salts. Individually, none of these substances is alive. Yet when each cell manufactures new protoplasm, using these substances, life is produced. Scientists have not yet been able to find out how this is accomplished.

One of the main problems is that the techniques used to analyze protoplasm destroy its "life" properties. Thus an entirely accurate analysis of protoplasm in the living state has not yet been possible.

It is hard to imagine the tremendous variety of cells. They may be any size from one ten-thousandth of an inch in diameter to the size of an ostrich egg, the largest single cell.

But no matter what size, shape, or color a living thing may be, it is composed of one or more cells. It is the cell that actually lives; every part of your body—and of the body of the dog and of the tree—that is alive is composed of cells. If the cells of your eyes die, you become blind; if your muscle cells die, you become paralyzed. You live because your cells live.

Plants and animals that are made of only one cell are called unicellular; those that are made of many cells are multicellular. Organisms (an organism is any form of animal or plant life) that are too small to be studied with the naked eye and so must be observed through a microscope are called **microorganisms**. **Microzoology** is the study of microscopic animals, and our "microzoo" will be populated by these tiny creatures.

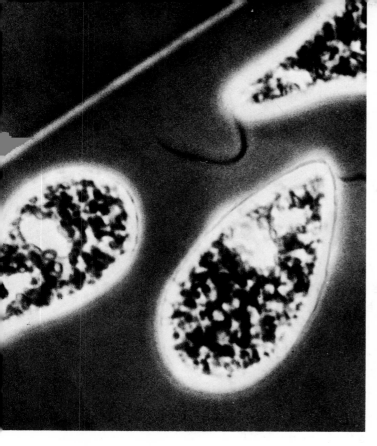

An interesting plant-animal, Euglena *is spindle-shaped, with a small depression or gullet at one end. Since it contains chlorophyll, it is able to manufacture its own food as plants do—that is, by photosynthesis. Carbohydrates are produced within the* Euglena *from carbon dioxide and water, in the presence of sunlight.*

Single-celled animals, or protozoa, are important members of the microzoo. There are some 50,000 different species of protozoa, and you cannot collect them all. But you will surely want to collect and study *Euglena, Amoeba,* and *Paramecium.* You can catch all of them in any fresh-water pond.

13

When we look at *Euglena* under a microscope, we see a one-celled organism which has a shape resembling a teardrop—rounded at one end and pointed at the other. Extending from the rounded end, or front, is a whiplike projection, or flagellum, with which the animal propels itself. Its body contains a red "eyespot" which is sensitive to light.

Euglena is an unusual member of the animal kingdom in that it is green in color. This is caused by the presence of chlorophyll, the substance which makes plants green. Thus the euglena is a kind of plant-animal. There are many of these one-celled organisms that possess both plant and animal characteristics. Scientists call them *Protista,* or protists.

Large clusters of *Euglenas* can easily be seen with the naked eye.

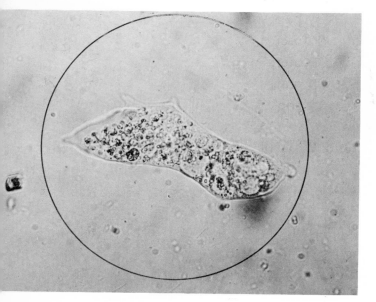

An amoeba is most often the animal that introduces the wonders of nature seen under the microscope lens. Observing this relatively simple organism, we can watch some of the functions of life, such as moving, eating, and reproduction, taking place in a single cell.

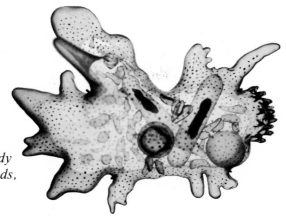

Amoebae capture food or move about by means of body extensions called pseudopods, or "false feet."

They form the greenish tinge of some ponds in the summer. You can scoop up some of these clusters with your hands and put them into a bottle with some of the water from the pond.

Amoebas, too, can be caught in summer ponds. They generally cluster on the under surface of water-lily pads or on the stems of water plants. To bring them home for a closer look, just put some bits of the water plants into a jar of pond water.

The amoeba, unlike *Euglena,* has no characteristic shape. However, if you will watch it under your microscope for a few moments, you will see that from time to time it extends a part of its body out into a pseudopod or false foot. After a while this shapeless extension goes back into the main body.

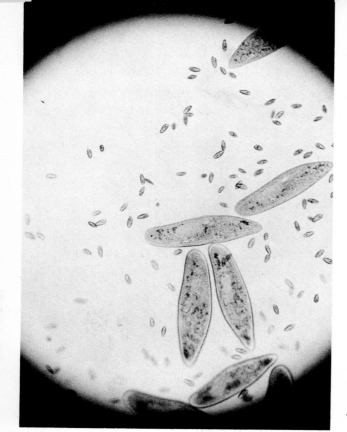

Paramecium is most often described as slipper- or cigar-shaped. Its outer surface is covered by many short, hairlike projections called cilia, which serve as a means of both locomotion and food gathering.

Paramecia may reproduce at a rate of 600 generations per year; if all were to live, at the end of five years their volume would be equal to 10^{1000} (that is, 10 followed by 1000 zeros) times the volume of the earth.

Paramecium is a slipper-shaped animal with hairlike projections from its edges called cilia, with which it propels itself. You can catch these creatures in almost any pond that contains weeds and animal life. If you fill a bottle with pond water there will doubtless be thousands of paramecia swimming around in it.

Besides the unicellular protozoa, you will also want to "capture" some of the multicellular forms, or metazoa. Going up the ladder of life forms, the first group of metazoan animals we come to consists of creatures which are little more than a colony of independent cells; these are the sponges. Next come the jellyfish, and in the same group with them is a microscopic animal called the hydra, which looks more like a plant than an animal.

Belonging to a group often referred to as the "flowers of the animal kingdom," hydras display some of the strangest shapes and most beautiful colors found in nature. To the naked eye, a hydra appears very much like a short, thin thread frazzled at the unattached end. Microscopic examination shows it to be a hollow tube, its mouth ringed with tentacles. When a hydra wishes to move from one place to another it may do so in several ways. It may glide slowly along on its foot or, more frequently, turn handsprings. To accomplish this the animal first bends over and attaches itself by its tentacles. The foot is released and the hydra contracts. It then expands, bends over in another direction, and attaches the foot. The tentacles now loosen their hold and the animal returns to an upright position.

Hydra is named for the nine-headed monster of Greek mythology. If one of the monster's heads was cut off, two more grew in its place. In laboratory experiments hydra has been cut up and the parts placed in a dish of water. A complete animal quickly formed from each piece. The favorite food of the hydra is the water flea or Daphnia. Here a hydra wraps its tentacles around its prey.

Progressing upward in complexity, we find the *Crustacea*, a group which includes the shrimp. Many of the very tiny creatures are not much larger than the protozoa and serve as food for small fish. Going on, we observe the *Arachnida*, to which belong spiders, scorpions, and ticks. Many in this group are microscopic in size.

Another group, *Insecta*, includes all insects, some of which produce young so tiny that magnification is necessary for proper study.

Proceeding to the fishes, we can get some idea of the small size of their young when we realize that one fish, depending on the particular type, can lay between 500 and several million eggs at one time.

These are just a few examples of the tiny plants and animals too small for us to see unaided. It is a tribute to man's genius that he has been able to develop instruments like the microscope to make visible this fascinating world which was once invisible. Come, let us explore it.

BRING 'EM BACK ALIVE

For your first hunting expedition you need only a few pieces of simple equipment—some widemouthed jars, a scoop net (which you can make yourself by bending a piece of wire into a hoop with a handle and attaching to it a piece of fine netting or a discarded nylon stocking), and perhaps a pocket magnifying lens.

Your "micro-jungle" is the nearest pond. Even a good-sized puddle will do. Take some of the water and examine it under a microscope. You will be able to see a variety of objects, including tiny one-celled plants, or algae, bits of soil, and parts of dead organisms. If you look carefully you will see that some of the objects

(left) A drop of water containing green algae, a protozoan, and blue-green algae. Algae are microscopic water plants which shelter many of the microzoo specimens described in this book. (right) Plants are the basis of life because they can change the energy of the sun into food. When animals eat plants, this food is changed back into energy. These flower-like plants are marine algae.

are moving about in the water. These moving objects are mostly micro-animals. Most of them will be one-celled protozoa.

One creature that is easily captured and kept is Daphnia, commonly called the water flea. The water flea can just be seen with the naked eye, jerking around near the surface of still pools where there are no fish. By running your scoop net through the water,

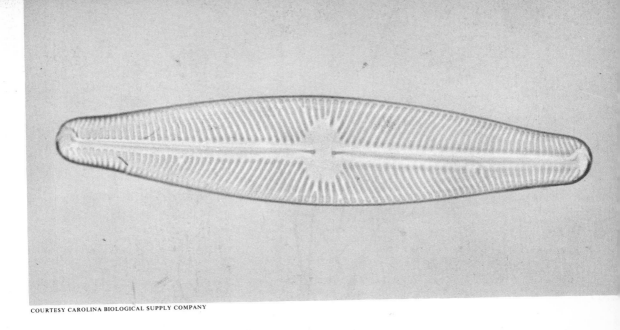

COURTESY CAROLINA BIOLOGICAL SUPPLY COMPANY

Diatoms are another type of algae, found in both fresh and salt water. Their geometric shape appears to have been made with mechanical precision, and is usually a variation of two basic types: the centric or pillbox type, and the pennate or shoebox type.

you should be able to pick up quite a few of these fellows. Carry them home in a jar half filled with water from the pond.

In order to keep them alive for future observation it is important to give them enough room and air. Large, flat dishes or trays like those for holding the solution used in developing photographs make fine homes for daphnias. The water they are kept in should

21

be cool, between 40° and 65° F., and the daphnias should have plenty of room to move around in.

They can be raised in a large jar of water and fed with the yolk of a hard-boiled egg. Mash the yolk with a teaspoon or two of water and keep the mixture in the refrigerator. Add a little to the daphnia jar every week or so. Add just enough to make the water slightly cloudy. When the water becomes clear, you will know that it is time to feed your daphnias again.

Probably the most common of the water fleas to be found in fresh water is Daphnia, *which reaches a length of just over one-eighth of an inch. Great numbers of these small crustaceans are eaten by fish, but the flea makes good the losses through rapid reproduction. Most of the year only females are in evidence. These produce, nearly every twelve days, about fifty eggs which develop without fertilization into more females. With the coming of fall, however, a brood of males develops which fertilizes a set of resistant "winter eggs" which hatch in the spring.*

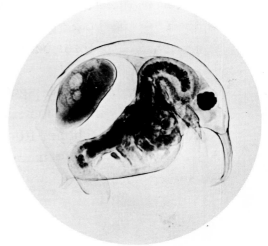

In the same pool as the daphnias you may also be able to find the larvae of the young of certain insects such as the mosquito or the midge. They usually float just below the surface of the water and must be scooped up quickly or they will escape to the bottom.

A fascinating creature to have in your microzoo is the hydra. Hydras are not easily found by beginning collectors, but they can be bought at a supply house (see list at end of book) and kept in a jar of water. They need live food and you can feed them daphnias. Use a medicine dropper or dipping tube to transfer a single daphnia into the hydra jar. If you can put the daphnia near it, you will see the hydra swallow it up very quickly.

Another good way of producing specimens for your microzoo is by means of infusions. Take a few large jars and fill them with rain water or boiled tap water. (Most tap water has chlorine in it which would kill protozoa before they even start growing. Boiling removes the chlorine.)

Let the water stand overnight and then put into each jar a small amount of infusion material, such as timothy hay, lettuce leaves, twigs, or dirt collected from a dried-up water puddle. Cover each jar and stand it by a window, but not directly in the sunlight. After a few days the water will get cloudy. This is caused by the growth of bacteria, microscopic plants. Soon after this, the infusion will begin to "come alive" with many types of protozoa.

These creatures came from little packets, known as cysts, in your infusion material. Lacking water to grow in, they encased themselves within thick cysts. In that inactive state they can survive many years, ready to spring to life when conditions are right. Your infusion has provided the proper conditions for them, and they revive and flourish.

You can follow the appearance of new forms in each infusion by examining drops of water each day with your microscope. You will be able to see dynasties emerge and pass away as different forms of protozoa become dominant in each infusion.

Compare the life in stagnant pond water with the findings in your infusion. Certain creatures will thrive better in one than in the other. Experiment with the effects of light and dark on your specimens. Take part of an infusion and put it into a closet, leaving the rest in the light. You will find that some animals prefer the dark. Try developing infusions with many different kinds of materials—various dried grasses, twigs from various places, soils from different areas. You will soon get to know many of the thousands of different protozoa.

When you find a particular species of protozoa that fascinates you, you may want to try to make a pure culture—that is, a culture that has only one particular kind of specimen in it. This requires some skill, but with practice it can be done. First you need a "soup" in which to grow your specimen. You can make this by boiling some dried grass, including some grass heads containing seeds, for about twenty minutes. After letting the mixture settle, fill a few small glass jars with the clear liquid from the top. Leave the jars for a few days where some light can enter them. Bacteria will grow in them and cover the surface of the water with grayish scum. This scum is your culture medium.

To make a pure culture you must drop into the culture medium a single protozoan. This is a tricky task, but not quite as hard as it sounds. You will need a capillary tube to do it. This can be purchased from any good laboratory supplier, and if there isn't one near you, you can write to one on the list at the back of this book. Or you can use an eye dropper, as shown in the accompanying photographs.

Take a protozoa-rich drop of water and let it run up into the small end of the capillary tube. By blowing through the big end you can scatter a number of little droplets onto a glass slide. Using the microscope (see next chapter), find a droplet that has but a single protozoan. You may have to repeat the process several

Using an eye dropper to isolate specimens from jar containing pond water. Rubber suction bulb draws up a sample containing minute forms of life to be observed.

times. After cleaning the tube thoroughly each time, let the droplet run up into it; then, by blowing through the big end, transfer the water to the medium.

Do this with several jars and several different types of protozoa to be sure of success. To be strictly scientific, all tubes, dishes, and jars should be sterilized by boiling for at least twenty minutes. Then leave one jar of soup with the others, but without a protozoan.

This jar is called the control. By the end of a week the control will still be without protozoa, but the other jars should be swarming with specimens, and if you have worked carefully, all those in each jar will be identical. Now you can be sure of getting precisely the specimen you want to see.

It is important to keep your collection well fed. As the culture develops, the food supply of bacteria will be used up. Every so often make a new batch of soup, and transfer a small part of the culture into the new medium. In this way you can keep a culture alive indefinitely.

When you have fully explored the possibilities in your stagnant pond, widen your field by collecting other specimens. One interesting fellow is a little eel that makes its home in unsterilized and unfiltered vinegar. Your grocer may have unfiltered vinegar, or else try your drugstore. If you hold some of this vinegar up to the light you will be able to see very tiny little lines wiggling about. Under your microscope these tiny lines will prove to be shaped like little eels, rounded at one end and pointed at the other, and marked all over by little dots. These dots are eggs which will hatch new eels. The vinegar eel is a true metazoan, not reproducing as protozoa do—by fission—but hatching from eggs like the higher animals.

Almost any place you go in nature you will find sources of supply for your microzoo, once you know how to look for them. For example, if you turn over a stone in a dim, well-watered area, you may be able to find a few samples of planaria, a flatworm. Another method of obtaining flatworms is to hang a small piece of meat into a slow-running stream. After a few hours take the meat from the water and you will probably find it covered with planaria.

The earliest forms of eyes and brains in the world are found in planaria. The eyes look like black dots along the sides of the back. Some kinds may have a hundred. Some have two eyes. Some have none at all.

When the tail of this planarian was carefully cut lengthwise in two sections, each half grew into a complete tail.

Keep them in about an inch of water. They will feed on small pieces of liver placed in the water. The meat should be taken out after feeding or it will decay and pollute the water.

Planaria are particularly interesting because of their regenerative capacity. If you cut one in half, each half will produce a whole new planarian like the original one. And if you carefully cut a planarian's head in half, in a few days you may have a planarian with two heads to photograph.

Pour some milk into a custard dish and let it stand without refrigeration for a few days. Put a drop of this milk on a slide and examine it under the microscope. It will show many interesting and different bacteria. If you make slides from samples of milk taken at different time intervals (for example: every three hours the first day, then once each day for two to three days), you will be able to follow the successive steps in the spoiling of milk. "Spoiled" food is the result of the activity of bacteria, (excessive multiplication creates waste matter, toxic to a degree that may be dangerous to man) and so is an interesting hunting ground for microbiologists. By making a microscope slide (see instructions in the next chapter) of the bacteria you can view and perhaps record on film what these forms of life are like.

A slide of a very small amount of garden soil dissolved in water can show you microbes existing in the ground. If you "plant" some of this soil-water solution on different nutrients, other soil microbes will show up under your microscope. You can purposely pollute milk or boiled water by adding a very small amount of soil. Examine slides made from the polluted milk or water and contrast them with pure samples.

If you live near the seashore you are near as rich a source of microzoo animals as any stagnant pond. Even if you do not, you may be able to raise at least one common form of salt-water creature, the baby shrimp. A full-grown shrimp is about two inches long, but the shrimp as it leaves its egg is small enough to be a member of the microzoo, and the opportunity to watch shrimp hatch should not be passed up.

Shrimp eggs can be obtained from a pet store that has a good stock of aquarium supplies. These eggs are in dried form. Before putting them in water, sprinkle a few on a slide and examine them. They look like pink or peach-colored ping-pong balls that someone has stepped on.

Now take some eggs, not too many, and drop them into a quart of water to which you have added a teaspoon of common table salt. It is important to keep the water warm, not letting the temperature drop below 70° F. Dip up some of the water with a few eggs and put it into a well slide. Watch it on and off for several hours. First the eggs will resume their original spherical shape. Then, in about four to eight hours, you will see them begin to split and the baby shrimp emerge.

At first the young shrimp are covered with a transparent membrane. This protects them until they have developed enough power in their feet to be able to swim. Sometime between fifteen and twenty-four hours after the experiment began, the shrimp will burst through the membrane. You will see them swimming freely in the water, propelling themselves by using their three pairs of legs as oars.

Place some of these newborn shrimp into a new medium of salt

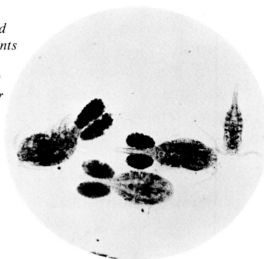

This tiny animal is a cyclops, named after the mythological one-eyed giants who helped Vulcan forge the thunderbolts of Zeus. An important part of the diet of many fresh-water fish, a cyclops rarely reaches one sixteenth of an inch in length, when it may be just visible to the naked eye. In this picture there are three females, each with two sacs of eggs, and one male.

and water, and put in a grain or two of dried yeast for food. You should be able to keep them alive for several weeks, watching them shed their skins two or three times as they grow. Transfer them into fresh warm salt water periodically, and add more yeast daily.

Another member of the class of *Crustacea,* besides the shrimp, is the cyclops. This tiny shellfish grows as long as one-sixteenth of an inch; at this size it may be just barely visible to the naked eye. Common in the fresh-water lakes and streams of North America, it is easily caught. If you collect a bottle of water from a lake or stream, you can see cyclopes swimming about in it. They will

32

appear as swiftly moving dots. Capture one with your capillary tube and put it in a well slide to examine under your microscope. If it is a female, you will see two sacs of eggs trailing behind its body. It is because it has only one eye that this tiny microlobster is called "cyclops," the name of the giant one-eyed monsters of Greek mythology.

A clump of moss will provide you with an opportunity to observe the tiny tardigrades, or water bears. They measure up to one twenty-fifth of an inch in length, and are therefore nearly invisible to the

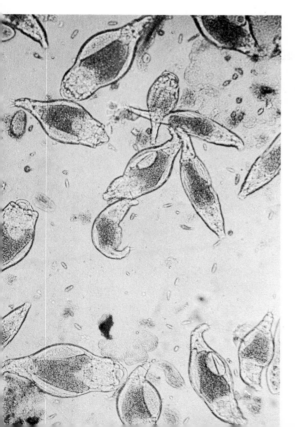

Among the most interesting of all the animals that can be observed under a microscope are the rotifers. Their name means "wheel bearers" and refers to the cilia found on their heads, whose shape and beating motion suggest the rotation of cogged wheels.

Rotifers are the smallest of the multi-celled animals, about equal in size to the average protozoan. The largest species is only one-fiftieth of an inch long. Rotifers exist mainly in fresh water. Of the seventeen hundred known species, only about fifty are found in the sea. A very few are able to exist on land, in damp places such as mosses.

naked eye. Any clump of moss should provide you with abundant specimens which you can watch under your microscope. They have fat little bodies with four pairs of stubby legs, each of which ends in a cluster of four or five tiny claws.

You will be able to bring back new specimens for your microzoo from almost every place you go. Here we have just mentioned the most common of the creatures you will find. Happy hunting—and don't forget to label your catch!

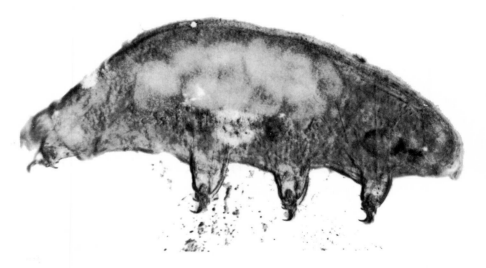

The tardigrades, or "water bears," have fat little bodies with four or five tiny claws. In times of drought they are able to expel body fluid and become dormant, in which state they can exist for years. Although most species are to be found in moss, some inhabit fresh-water ponds and others are marine. The salt-water forms creep about on the water film between grains of wet sand, or cling to the bodies of sea cucumbers, sea fans, and other slow-moving or attached animals. They are also called "bear animalcules."

YOUR MICROSCOPE

Of course one cannot enjoy a microzoo unless one has a microscope with which to see it. A microscope is really any instrument used to help see very small things. The simplest microscope is an ordinary pocket lens or "magnifying glass." The most complex is the electron microscope, which is used to examine the smallest life forms. Both work on the same simple principles.

How does a microscope "enlarge" things? It does so by using the ability of the lens to bend light waves. When we see something, we do not really see the object itself, but only light waves reflected from the object. When we look at something through

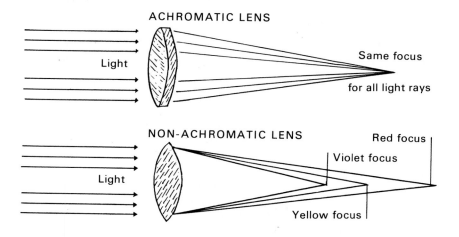

ACHROMATIC LENS

Light

Same focus

for all light rays

NON-ACHROMATIC LENS

Red focus

Violet focus

Light

Yellow focus

a microscope, the light waves coming from the object must pass through the lens. Light waves usually travel in straight lines, but when they reach the microscope lens they are "bent," or redirected. Thus, when the waves reach your eye they occupy a larger percentage of the area your eye can see than they would have if they had come straight from the object. In this way the object appears to be enlarged.

The eye, in order to catch the reflected light, must be at the point behind the lens where all the light is concentrated. This point is called the **focus** of the lens.

You will probably be using a **compound microscope.** This consists of two simple magnifying lenses. The **power** of a microscope tells you how much an object seems to be enlarged. A

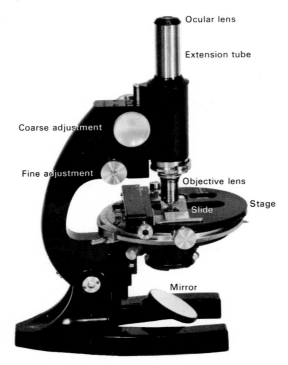

Ocular lens

Extension tube

Coarse adjustment

Fine adjustment

Objective lens

Slide

Stage

Mirror

A microscope is a precision instrument, not a toy. Always lift it by the upright, to minimize damage to other parts. Keep the lenses clean with lens-cleaning paper, and avoid leaving finger prints on lens surface. Protect your microscope by keeping it covered or in its case. Never take the microscope apart.

10X lens (or "10-power lens") will make an insect, for example, one-tenth of an inch long appear ten times as big, or one inch long. Thus the power of a compound microscope is the product of the power of its lenses. For instance: if your lenses are 10X and 15X, the magnification will be 10 multiplied by 15, or 150X.

You need not have an expensive microscope, but caution should be exercised before you buy one. The cheapest microscope may have very bad lenses, and be almost impossible to use properly. You will probably be able to purchase an instrument for about fifteen dollars which will suit your purpose. A second-hand microscope, if the lenses are not damaged and the adjustments work properly, will do nicely.

Microscopes which have lenses of great magnification should be avoided, since these lenses will be too complicated for the amateur. Also you should check to be sure your lenses are **achromatic.** Achromatic means colorless, but it is the term applied to lenses that are corrected in order to transmit color without distortion. When ordinary light, as from the sun or a light bulb, hits a piece of curved glass such as a lens, the white light is broken up into the colors of the rainbow. If you have a non-achromatic lens on your microscope the same sort of thing will happen, and you will be able to see only a blurred image.

The two lenses of the microscope are the **ocular,** which is close to the eye, and the **objective,** which is close to the speci-men. They are set in a tube that moves up and down in a frame attached to the base of the microscope. The movement is con-trolled by two knobs, the **coarse adjustment** and the **fine ad-justment.** Beneath the objective is the **stage,** which is simply a platform through which a hole has been drilled.

Beneath the stage, set so that it can be turned at various angles, is a mirror that reflects light through the hole in the stage. This light is extremely important, for it is what illuminates what you are looking at.

A ten-watt bulb placed a few inches from the mirror is usually enough. It should give you a steady light that does not hurt your eyes when you look through the microscope. Later you may want to purchase a **sub-stage light,** a light source that attaches to the bottom of the stage and eliminates the need for the mirror.

Remember that your microscope is a scientific instrument. Certain techniques must be developed to use it properly. You should accustom yourself to looking through the microscope and getting the feel of the instrument before you begin to experi-ment with it. Both eyes should be kept open when viewing, to prevent eyestrain later on. This technique can be developed with practice.

The microscope never should be focused downward toward

the specimen being viewed. Instead, bring the extension tube down as far as it will go without touching the specimen on the stage. Looking at the tube from the side while you focus downward will allow you to stop before the objective makes contact.

Now look through the eyepiece, bringing the extension tube upward slowly, using the coarse adjustment. As soon as you see forms appear, switch to the fine adjustment. Before trying to examine your specimens for details, focus as sharply as possible. With a little practice you will be able to focus quickly and accurately.

It is a good idea to learn how your microscope is constructed. This will enable you to make minor repairs on your instrument, and will save you money. For instance, instead of buying a microscope with more than one objective lens mounted on a turret (such a "revolving nosepiece" usually has three objectives), you can purchase the extra objectives separately at a great saving.

You can take out and put in your different objectives at will, but in the beginning you should view the specimen first through the lens of smallest magnification. The area viewed through the microscope is called the **field.** The bigger the magnification, the smaller the field becomes, so using your weakest lens will allow you to cover the greatest area of the specimen.

Always keep the microscope covered when not in use. This will prevent dust from accumulating on the lenses. The lenses should be cleaned periodically. Never touch them with your fingers. Use a soft cloth or lens tissue. Lens tissues can be purchased at any laboratory supply store.

PREPARING YOUR MICROZOO SPECIMENS

Now you are ready to observe a drop of your pond water. But you cannot simply put the drop of water on a slide, cover it with a **cover slip** (a thin piece of glass placed over the specimen), and begin observing. The weight of the slip, slight though it is, will crush many of the larger creatures you would find in a drop of pond water. You will need special "depression slides" that have a little hollow well in them. These can be purchased easily and inexpensively, or can be made from regular slides quite easily. The object is to provide the specimens with a small pool in which they can swim freely. Their swimming pool can be constructed on the slide by attaching to the slide a small piece or two of cardboard with a circle punched out of the center. The best adhesive for your purposes is shellac. When it dries the cardboard will be firmly attached and waterproofed as well.

Slips, or cover glasses, come in several different sizes, and are usually sold by weight. A half ounce may contain a hundred cover

Placing a drop of water on a slide, this student is about to observe minute plants and animals unknown to the naked eye.

A homemade well slide, easily made by shellacking to the glass a square of cardboard with a hole punched out of it. Accessories are forceps (tweezers) and a probe (needle inserted into wooden handle).

glasses and will cost only a dollar or so. It is a good investment, especially when you begin making permanent slides. You will be able to start viewing by simply placing a drop of water in the well.

You will probably notice after observing a water drop for some time that the water will begin to evaporate around the edges of your cover glass. To remedy this, keep a small dish of water handy, and every so often dip a small brush into it. By placing the bristles at the edge of the slip, you can keep your well from running dry. A process of absorption called **capillary action** will draw the water under the slip and into the well.

You may want to keep a particular specimen overnight, to show to someone or to examine more closely at your leisure. To prevent the well from drying up, place the slide over a small dish half filled with water. Make a wick by rolling some absorbent cotton into a thread between your fingers. Place it over the slide so that it touches the edge of the cover slide and both ends hang down into the water. Capillary action will draw water through the wick and into the well, keeping your specimen fresh.

In many cases you will want to make permanent slides of particular specimens. These permanent slides are known as **mounts.** A mount is usually made by attaching a cover slip to a slide with

Cotton wick leading from dish of water keeps specimens moist.

Head of a flea, one of the Insecta, *which are air-breathing creatures with piercing and sucking mouth parts. The insects are the largest group of animal life. Over 700,000 species have been discovered, and there are probably thousands more still to be identified.*

either balsam or glycerine. Both of these materials are inexpensive and easily obtained at all laboratory supply stores. They adhere glass to glass and will preserve your specimens. Most important, they will not distort the field because they are transparent and practically colorless.

While some specimens, such as the flea head in the photograph, can be mounted immediately, most need first to be dried, or dehydrated. The reason for this is that water will quickly destroy a mounted specimen, and most cells—and that includes protozoa—contain water. To prevent this destruction, substitute alcohol for water. Alcohol will strengthen the cell walls and prevent decay. However, alcohol cannot merely be poured on a specimen, for this would harden the cell walls immediately, trapping water inside. Instead, alcohol must be substituted for water gradually. This is known as **fixing**. It is a good method for preserving specimens of the larger members of the microzoo, such as insects. Sections of larger insects, such as the grasshopper, may be preserved, while smaller insects like the flea may be preserved whole.

To fix a specimen, place it on a slide, and upon it one drop of alcohol and three drops of water. After ten minutes repeat the proc-

A commercial well slide containing a specimen being fixed, or preserved, by the addition of alcohol

47

A wire loop is used to control spreading of specimens on slide.

ess, using two drops of alcohol and two of water. Continue until you are using pure alcohol. In about an hour your specimen will be fixed and ready for mounting.

Another way of mounting is the **smear technique.** This involves spreading a bit of some thick culture on a slide and holding it over a flame until it has been thoroughly dried. Balsam or glycerine and a cover glass may then be applied as described above. The smear technique is the proper technique for preserving tiny creatures like protozoa, and is used when we grow our own microbe "gardens." The wire loop is the tool used to help make these smears. The loop, which can be bought in any laboratory supply store, is a piece of wire bent to a small circle at the end and attached to a heat-resistant handle. It looks like a small "b" when the loop is held downward. By using this tool's edge, you can scrape off bacteria colonies or mold and put them directly on the slide.

Another method, used more often, is to take part of a bacteria colony or mold and add it to distilled water. (You may purchase

This young lady is using a magnifying glass and a probe to separate microzoo candidates. Eye dropper will suck up water and animal to be placed on slide for observation under microscope lens.

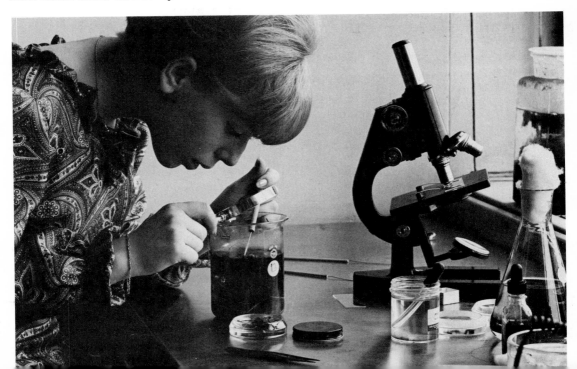

distilled water cheaply at the grocery or drug store or obtain it from the science lab in your school.)

Adding the bacteria or mold to the water and then extracting just a drop of the water, spreading it on a slide, and fixing it will give you a better chance to view a single bacterium or mold.

In many cases your specimen will not reveal its parts clearly under the microscope. To overcome this, you can use various coloring materials known as **stains.** There are many different types of stains, and each is useful for different objects. When applied they will color certain parts of the specimen so that they are visible under the microscope.

There are many different stains you can use. Most of the readily available and easy-to-use stains that you will be trying at first contain poisons which kill the organisms. Among these stains are iodine, Mercurochrome, Merthiolate, and fountain-pen ink.

A common stain that will not kill the organisms is **methylene blue;** another is **eosin,** the red stain used in most brands of red inks.

Occasionally India ink is used as a stain, especially when examining small transparent specimens. India ink is a **negative stain**— that is, it colors the background rather than the specimen itself, so that the specimen appears as a light area against a field of dark gray.

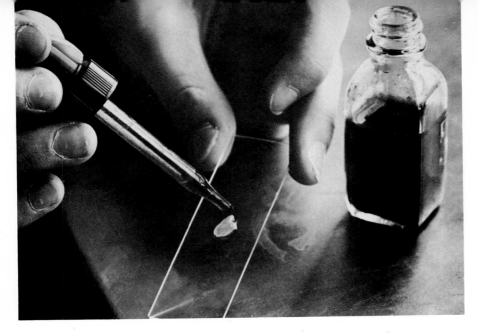

A drop of ink is being placed at the edge of a specimen mounted on a slide to give contrast to parts nearly invisible. This technique is called "staining."

To apply the stain, place a drop at the very edge of the cover. This drop will gradually work its way through the water beneath the cover by the process of **diffusion.** As it comes into contact with the organisms in the water they will be stained.

By experimenting with different stains and photographing the results as described in the following chapter, you may record interesting contrasts.

PHOTOGRAPHING YOUR MICROZOO

Exploring the world of the microzoo with your microscope is a fascinating and rewarding experience. Photographing this world can add greatly to your enjoyment and understanding. It enables you to keep a permanent record of your finds, and makes it possible for you to display them in science fairs.

By adjusting your camera to work with the microscope, you can make exciting pictures of your microzoo. The technique of making such pictures through a microscope is known as **photomicrography.**

You will not be able just to hold your camera over the microscope and take pictures. However, with a little care you can adapt your camera for this purpose and take reasonably good photographs.

A **retaining ring** and an **adapter ring,** which may be purchased inexpensively from any camera store, adapt your camera for photomicrography. Black masking tape may also be used as a temporary means of making a light-tight fit between the camera's shutter and the microscope eyepiece, called the **ocular.** An ordinary laboratory ring stand makes an ideal camera support.

Focus the microscope to create a sharp image of your subject. Remove the ocular from the microscope and fasten it to the camera lens by using the adapter ring threaded into the retaining ring. Replace the ocular, with camera attached, in the microscope. Now

*The adapter ring, retaining ring, and inner tube attachment
needed to adapt a simple camera to a microscope*

Placing a simple camera with microscope attachments into the tube. Cameras with ground-glass features permit more precise adjustment and focus, and enable you to see and arrange your composition better.

carefully snap the shutter to make the exposure. You can minimize the possibility of camera movement by using a **cable release.**

If your camera has a ground glass for focusing, it will be simple to obtain a sharp image by using only the focusing adjustments of the microscope. Turn the coarse-adjustment knob slowly toward you so as to raise the tube. When the object appears to be clearly defined, use the fine adjustment to get it sharp. To avoid

Black masking tape is used to improvise a light-tight fit between camera and microscope tube. Cable release in hand minimizes vibration. Magnifying glass aids in composition.

cracking a valuable slide or damaging a still more valuable objective lens, always "focus up." If you have a simple box camera it will be necessary to determine the **eyepoint**—that is, the place above the ocular where the image is located. To do this, move a piece of tissue paper up and down above the eyepiece until you find the place where the light coming through the microscope comes to a point. The center of the front lens of the camera should be placed precisely at this point, and the axes of the camera and microscope should be aligned.

Your lens diaphragm should be "wide open" at the largest aperture. Focus is at infinity. Fixed-focus cameras usually have only one shutter speed—about one-fiftieth of a second—which requires a very bright light source, correctly adjusted. Photographs made in color present additional problems, particularly because exposures must be very accurate. If your light source is daylight or an

Adjusting the microscope by always "focusing up." Paper and pencil are indispensable for recording observations.

electronic flash, which is now so popular (but expensive), use outdoor color film. If you use incandescent bulbs, use indoor color film. If your exposures appear to be correct but the colors are "too cold" (excessive blue) or "too warm" (excessive red, etc.), correct this by using gelatin filters recommended by the manufacturer and obtainable from your camera dealer.

You will simply have to experiment with various films, lights, and exposures to obtain the best results. Keep notes of your exposure time, trying various speeds including short time exposures. Measure your light source with an exposure meter to determine its strength, or note the distance of the light from microscope in inches, so that you may readily duplicate the lighting. Use any film you have become accustomed to using. Depending on the results you may be after, you may later wish to experiment with faster films (usually producing a grainy effect) or slower films (which are fine-grain). These are some of the factors that determine the quality of the photomicrograph.

Presenting your work for exhibit in school or at science fairs is not difficult. You need not photograph every specimen or microscope slide. Select the most dramatic ones to explain your whole experiment. Sketches and written material can be mounted alongside the enlarged photographs.

Photo-finishing houses will enlarge and print small negatives for you. Enlargements ten to thirty times the original will cost from one to ten dollars. They may be mounted on cardboard or masonite. Just think what a water drop from a pond stocked with protozoa looks like when the small microscope field, one inch in diameter, is blown up to thirty inches!

A drop of pond water magnified one hundred diameters

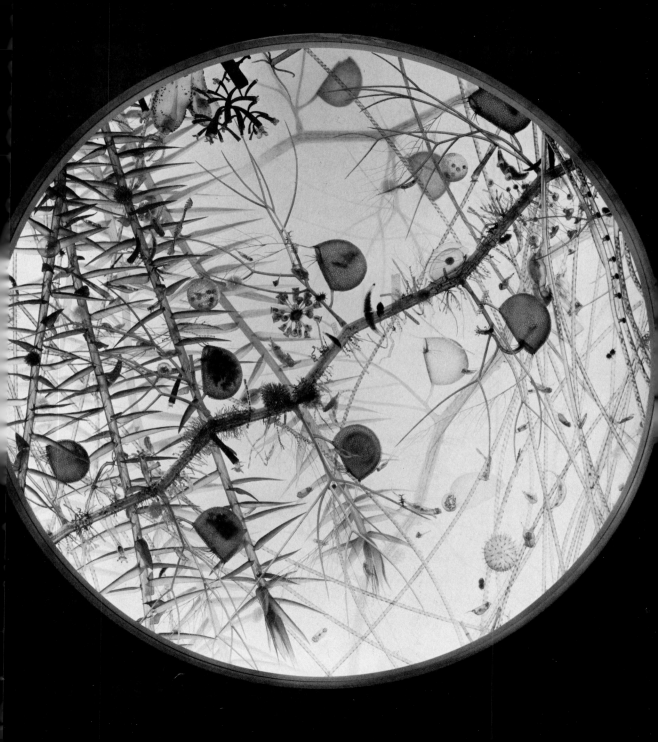

American Optical Company, Buffalo 15, New York
   Microscopes and optical accessories

Bausch & Lomb Optical Company, Rochester, New York
   Microscopes, magnifiers, etc.

Carolina Biological Supply Company, Elon College, North Carolina
   Microscopic specimens, living or preserved

Central Scientific Company, 1700 Irving Park Road, Chicago 13, Illinois
   Prepared slides of microscopic organisms

Chicago Apparatus Company, 1735 North Ashland Avenue, Chicago 13, Illinois
   Complete source of biological supplies

Ercona Corporation, 527 Fifth Avenue, New York 17, New York
   Microscopes and optical accessories

Fisher Scientific Company, 717 Forges Street, Pittsburgh 19, Pennsylvania
   Complete source of biological supplies

General Biological Supply House, Inc., 8200 South Hoyne Avenue, Chicago 20, Illinois
   Complete source of biological supplies

Gotham Scientific Company, 106 Water Street, New York 5, New York
   Complete laboratory accessories, slides of microscopic organisms

Marine Biological Laboratory, Woods Hole, Massachusetts
   Living microscopic specimens, marine species

Quivira Specialties Company, 4204 West 21st Street, Topeka, Kansas
   Biological specimens, living or preserved

Ross, Harry, 61 Reade Street, New York 7, New York
    Biological specimens, optical equipment

Scientific Laboratory Supply Company, 139 Forrest Avenue N.E., Atlanta, Georgia
    Complete source of biological supplies

Standard Scientific Supply Corporation, 34 West 4th Street, New York 12, New York
    Complete source of biological supplies

United Scientific Company, 204 Milk Street, Boston 9, Massachusetts
    Complete source of biological supplies

Ward's Natural Scientific Establishment, Inc., 3000 Ridge Road East, Rochester 9, New York
    Complete source of biological supplies

SUGGESTIONS FOR FURTHER READING

Allen, R. M. *The Microscope.* Princeton, New Jersey: D. Van Nostrand Co., Inc., 1940.

Barer, R. *Lecture Notes on the Use of the Microscope.* Philadelphia: Blackwell Scientific Publications, 1962.

Beeler, Nelson F., and Franklyn M. Branley. *Experiments With a Microscope.* New York: Thomas Y. Crowell Co., 1957.

Beiser, Arthur. *Guide to the Microscope.* New York: E. A. Dutton & Co., 1957.

Bragg, W. *Universe of Light.* New York: Dover Publications, Inc., 1959.

Corrington, J. D. *Exploring With Your Microscope.* New York: McGraw-Hill Book Co., Inc., 1957.

Cosgrove, Margaret. *Strange Worlds Under a Microscope.* New York: Dodd, Mead & Co., 1957.

————, *Wonders Under a Microscope*. New York: Dodd, Mead & Co., 1957.

Darling, Lois, and Louis Darling. *The Science of Life*. Cleveland: The World Publishing Co.,1961.

Disraeli, Robert. *New Worlds Through the Microscope*. New York: The Viking Press, 1960.

Eastman Kodak Company. *Photography Through the Microscope*. Rochester, 1962.

Gage, S. H. *The Microscope*. Ithaca, New York: Comstock Publishing Associates, 1951.

Garnett, William J. *Freshwater Microscopy*. New York: Dover Publications, Inc., 1953.

Hartley, W. G., Bernard Friedman, and John J. Lee. *How to Use a Microscope*. Garden City, N.Y.: Natural History Press, 1964.

Headstrom, Richard. *Adventures With a Microscope*. Philadelphia: J. B. Lippincott Co., 1962.

Johnson, Gaylord, and Maurice Bleifeld. *Hunting With the Microscope*. New York: Sentinel Books, 1963.

Lonert, A. C. *Turtox Microscopy*. Chicago: General Biological Supply, 1946.

Munoz, Frank J., and Harry A. Charipper. *The Microscope and Its Use*. New York: Chemical Publishing Co., 1943.

Needham, G. H. *Practical Use of the Microscope*. Springfield, Illinois: C. C. Thomas Co., 1958.

Pyszkowski, Irene S. *The Microscope and a Hidden World to Explore*. Racine, Wisconsin: Whitman Publishing Co., 1962.

Shillaber, C. P. *Photomicrography*. New York: John Wiley & Sons, Inc., 1944.

Simpson, George Gaylord, C. S. Pittendrigh, and L. H. Tiffany. *Life: An Introduction to Biology*. New York: Harcourt, Brace & Co., 1957.

Weesner, Frances M. *General Zoological Microtechniques*. Baltimore, Md.: Williams & Wilkins Co., 1960.

MEET ROY PINNEY

Armed with cameras, notebook, and tape recorder, photo-naturalist Roy Pinney travels all over the world for his stunning photographs which appear in scientific articles and magazine advertisements. In his long photographic career he has worked for a newspaper, for *Life, Look, The Saturday Evening Post,* and other periodicals; has filmed several television series, and is currently a well-known lecturer and a columnist for *U. S. Camera Magazine.* His many awards include first prize from *Popular Photography Magazine,* from Graflex and Ansco, and the Gold Medal Award of the New York Art Directors' Club.

At one time the Brooklyn Museum's Curator for Natural History, Mr. Pinney is the author-illustrator of a number of books. With his wife, herself a famous photographer, and their four photogenic children, he lives in Larchmont, New York.

1   2   3   4   5   69   68   67   66   65